Alphabet Affirmations

for

Boys

of

Color

Alfreida McKinney

Life Chronicles Publishing

ISBN-978-1-950649-27-3

Cover Design: Life Chronicles Publishing

Illustrations: Life Chronicles Publishing

Life Chronicles Publishing © 2020

lifechroniclespublishing.com

Dedication

To my son, Joshua - and all of the amazingly beautiful and courageous boys of color.

I am artistic, amazing and active

B

I am brave, blissful and blessed

C

I am caring, creative and confident

D

I am driven, dazzling and divine

E

I am encouraged, energetic and empathetic

F

I am fantastic, focused and fearless

G

I am graceful, grateful and gifted

I am humble, helpful and hopeful

I

I am inspired, innovative and independent

J

I am joyous, jolly and jubilant

K

I am kind, keen and knowledgeable

L

I am loving, legendary and lively

I am magical, mindful and motivated

I am noble, nurturing and notable

I am open, optimistic and observant

I am persistent, proud and phenomenal

I am quick-thinking and I ask questions

I am respectful, radiant and remarkable

S

I am successful, soulful and supportive

T

I am talented, tenacious and terrific

I am upbeat, unique and understanding

I am vibrant, valuable and virtuous

I am worthy, welcoming and wonderful

I am eXquisite, eXtraordinary and eXceptional

I am youthful and happY

Z

I am zestful and zappy

Made in the USA
Las Vegas, NV
23 September 2022

55784193R00019